This book belongs to

....

Walt Disney's

Goofy Movie Star

Storybook Favourites

Reader's Digest Young Families

Walt Disney's
Goofy Movie Star

Illustrations by The Walt Disney Studios

Story adapted by Annie North Bedford

Illustrations adapted by Samuel Armstrong

Once upon a time there was a wonderful place called Hollywood.

It was the centre of Movie Land.

Everyone in Hollywood, it seemed, wanted to be a Movie Star.

Every waitress was waiting to be discovered, so she could be a Starlet for a Movie Studio.

Every young man working at a petrol station planned to grow up to be a Movie Star.

They were all waiting for a Talent Scout to happen along. For a Talent Scout is a man, you know, who finds new Movie Stars.

Driving down the streets of Hollywood, you knew at once you were in Movie Land. You almost wanted to be a Movie Star, too.

There was just one person in Hollywood, it seemed, who didn't care about being a Movie Star.

His name was Dippy Dog. And he was a happy soul.

Dippy liked the movies, of course. He liked to sit in the balcony seats with a bag of popcorn and settle down to watch a film.

'Yuk yuk yuk!' he would laugh his merry laugh. And everyone around would laugh with him.

One night some Talent Scouts heard Dippy laugh.
'Who is that laughing?' they cried. 'He has the
makings of a Movie Star!'

And when they found it was Dippy Dog, the Talent
Scouts hustled him off to a Movie Studio. They didn't
even wait for Dippy to see the rest of the film. Talent
Scouts waste no time!

Soon Dippy was signing a contract to be a Movie Star.
'What's your name, son?' said the producer. 'Dippy
Dog? That will never do!'

'We need a name that breathes romance – Dandy – Daffy – Goofy! That's it!'

So Goofy signed his new name to the contract. And then he was a Movie Star.

Now Goofy had to dress like a Movie Star. He had whole wardrobes full of clothes.

And he had to have some shiny new cars – not one new car but four!

He had to move from his little house to a mansion
worthy of a movie star.

It had a swimming pool for each day of the week.

And there was a special pool for Saturdays.

Goofy had to have his picture taken, of course. He had his picture taken waking up, eating his breakfast – even brushing his teeth.

He had his picture taken dressed for golf – and tennis and hopscotch and polo.

Goofy was so busy having pictures taken for newspapers and magazines and television shows, that he never had time to actually play.

He even had pictures taken for a Movie. He was the Star, of course.

Now, whenever he went to eat in a restaurant, Movie
Fans waited at the door, to see him walk in and out.

The night his Movie opened, all the pretty girls and handsome young men who wanted to be Movie Stars too lined up outside the theatre.

'Isn't he wonderful?' they said. 'How did he do it?'
Then along came a famous newspaper journalist to interview the new Star.
'What is the secret of your success?' she asked.

'Yuk yuk yuk!' laughed Goofy – the laugh that made him famous. 'I guess I just have fun, that's all.'

And that is the story of how Goofy became a Movie Star in Hollywood, once upon a time.

Walt Disney's Goofy Movie Star is a *Disney Storybook Favourites* book

Walt Disney's Goofy Movie Star, copyright © 1956, 2006 Disney Enterprises, Inc.
Story adapted by Annie North Bedford. Illustrations adapted by Samuel Armstrong.

This edition was adapted and published in 2009 by
The Reader's Digest Association Limited
11 Westferry Circus, Canary Wharf, London E14 4HE

Editor: Rachel Warren Chadd
Designer: Louise Turpin
Design consultant: Simon Webb

® Reader's Digest, the Pegasus logo and Reader's Digest Young Families
are registered trademarks of
The Reader's Digest Association, Inc.

We are committed both to the quality of our products
and the service we provide to our customers.
We value your comments, so please do contact us on
08705 113366 or via our website at
www.readersdigest.co.uk
If you have any comments or suggestions
about the content of our books, email us at
gbeditorial@readersdigest.co.uk

Printed in China

A Disney Enterprises/Reader's Digest Young Families Book

ISBN 978 0 276 44473 9
Book code 641-032 UP0000-1
Oracle code 504400087H.00.24